# Classroom Jams
## Pop Hits

Published by
**Wise Publications**
14-15 Berners Street, London W1T 3LJ, UK.

Exclusive Distributors:
**Music Sales Limited**
Distribution Centre, Newmarket Road, Bury St Edmunds,
Suffolk IP33 3YB, UK.
**Music Sales Pty Limited**
120 Rothschild Avenue, Rosebery, NSW 2018, Australia.

This book © Copyright 2007 Chester Music,
a division of Music Sales Limited.
Order No. CH72655
ISBN: 978-1-84772-172-3

Arranged by Barrie Carson Turner.
Music processed by Paul Ewers Music Design.
Edited by Rachel Payne.
Cover designed by Liz Barrand.
Printed in the EU.

This publication is not authorised for sale in
the United States of America and /or Canada

**Your Guarantee of Quality**
As publishers, we strive to produce every book to the
highest commercial standards.
This book has been carefully designed to minimise
awkward page turns and to make playing from it a real
pleasure.
Particular care has been given to specifying acid-free,
neutral-sized paper made from pulps which have not
been elemental chlorine bleached.
This pulp is from farmed sustainable forests and was
produced with special regard for the environment.
Throughout, the printing and binding have been planned
to ensure a sturdy, attractive publication which should
give years of enjoyment.
If your copy fails to meet our high standards, please
inform us and we will gladly replace it.

www.musicsales.com

**Wise Publications**
part of The Music Sales Group

London / New York / Paris / Sydney / Copenhagen / Berlin / Madrid / Tokyo

# A NOTE FOR TEACHERS

The choice of instrumentation for these arrangements has been left to the teacher, though suggestions for percussion are given in each piece. The idea behind the arrangements is that they are playable on whatever instruments are available and parts are differentiated in difficulty so everyone can join in!

The Melody and Harmony parts go no lower than Middle C or higher than A, an octave and a half above, and are therefore particularly suited to Recorder, Violin, Flute and Tuned Percussion. (Flautists may occasionally prefer to play at a higher octave.) The arrangements will also work well with keyboards (one hand) taking any or all of the parts.

Generally, Harmony 2 part is easier than Harmony 1, and most often likely to be the lower part. However, all parts do occasionally cross.

Guitar chords are included and could be used by guitarists or keyboard players. To keep these as simple as possible, inversions have been omitted. The letter names of the chords may be played as a bass part (bass xylophone, cello, etc).

Have fun!

# Don't Look Back In Anger

Words & Music by Noel Gallagher

Suggested Percussion:
Chime or Glockenspiel (Ch/Gl)
Cym (Cym)
Drum (Dr)

# All About You

Words & Music by Thomas Fletcher

**Suggested Percussion:**
Claves or Woodblocks (Cl/Wb)
Shakers (Sh)
Chinese Bells (CB)
Cow Bell (B)

# Feeling Good

Words & Music by Leslie Bricusse & Anthony Newley

Suggested Percussion:
Chime or Glockenspiel (Ch/Gl)
Tambourine (Tb)

11

# HAPPY TOGETHER

Words & Music by Garry Bonner & Alan Gordon

**Suggested Percussion:**
Drum (Dr)
Tambourine (Tbn)
Cowbell (B)
Cymbal (Cym)

14

# Hey Jude

Words & Music by John Lennon & Paul McCartney

**Suggested Percussion:**
Triangle (Tr)
Chime or Glockenspiel (Ch/Gl)
Tambourine (Tbn)
Shakers (Sh)

# I'M A BELIEVER

Words & Music by Neil Diamond

Suggested Percussion:
Tambourine (Tbn)
Drum played with fingers (Dr)

# It Must Be Love

Words & Music by Labi Siffre

**Suggested Percussion:**
Tambourine (Tbn)
Scraper (Scr)
Cowbell (B)
Shakers (Sh)

# LOVE IS ALL AROUND

Words & Music by Reg Presley

**Suggested Percussion:**
Claves or Woodblocks (Cl/Wb)
Cymbal (Cym)
Tambourine (Tbn)

**Moderately slow**

*To Coda* ⊕

**D.S. al Coda**   ⊕ **Coda**
rit.

# Somethin' Stupid

Words & Music by C. Carson Parks

Suggested Percussion:
Cymbal (Cym)
Claves or Woodblocks (Cl/Wb)
Shakers (Sh)

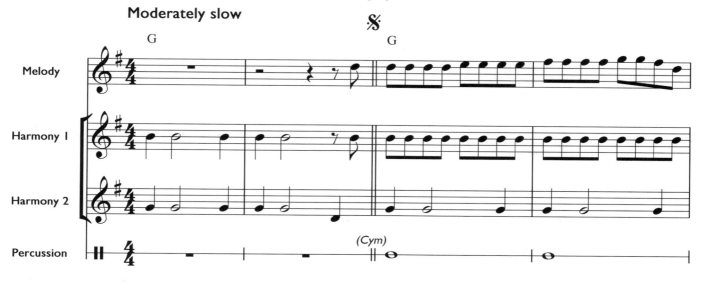

# TALK

Words & Music by Guy Berryman, Chris Martin, Karl Bartos, Jon Buckland, Will Champion, Emil Schult & Ralf Hütter

**Suggested Percussion:**
Chime or Glockenspiel (Ch/Gl)
Tambourine (Tbn)
Claves or Woodblocks (Cl/Wb)

**Moderate beat**

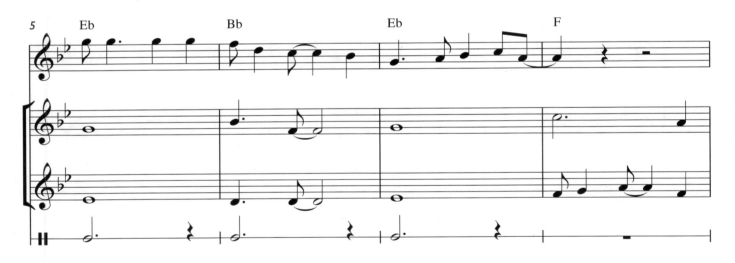

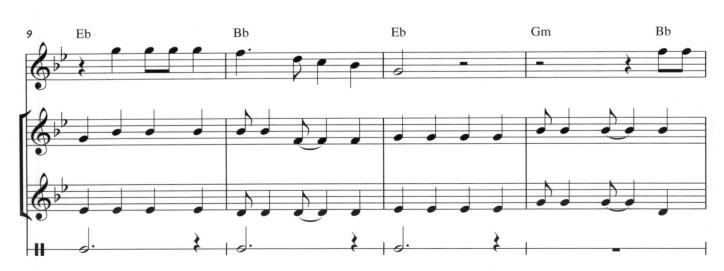

31

123456789